A Flurry of Fall Fun

Cover Art by Bob Berry
Editorial by Leigh Heather Wilson

© 2003, 2004, 2005 Modern Publishing, a division of Unisystems, Inc.

Modern Publishing
A Division of Unisystems, Inc.
New York, New York 10022

Printed in the U.S.A.

Series UPC: 49245

The signs of fall are all around!

Tommi chooses an outfit for the first day.

A Picnic in the Park

The Start of a School Year

1. COUNTY FAIR

Tommi and her brother went to the country fair. How many buckets of apples do you see? How many pies? How many wreaths?

See Answers

2. A CRISP FALL DAY

There are many things you can do in the fall. Look at the pictures. Circle the ones that show things you can do in the fall.

See Answers

"There goes a rabbit!"

A Visit from Grandpa and Grandma

Grandma knit Tommi a sweater.

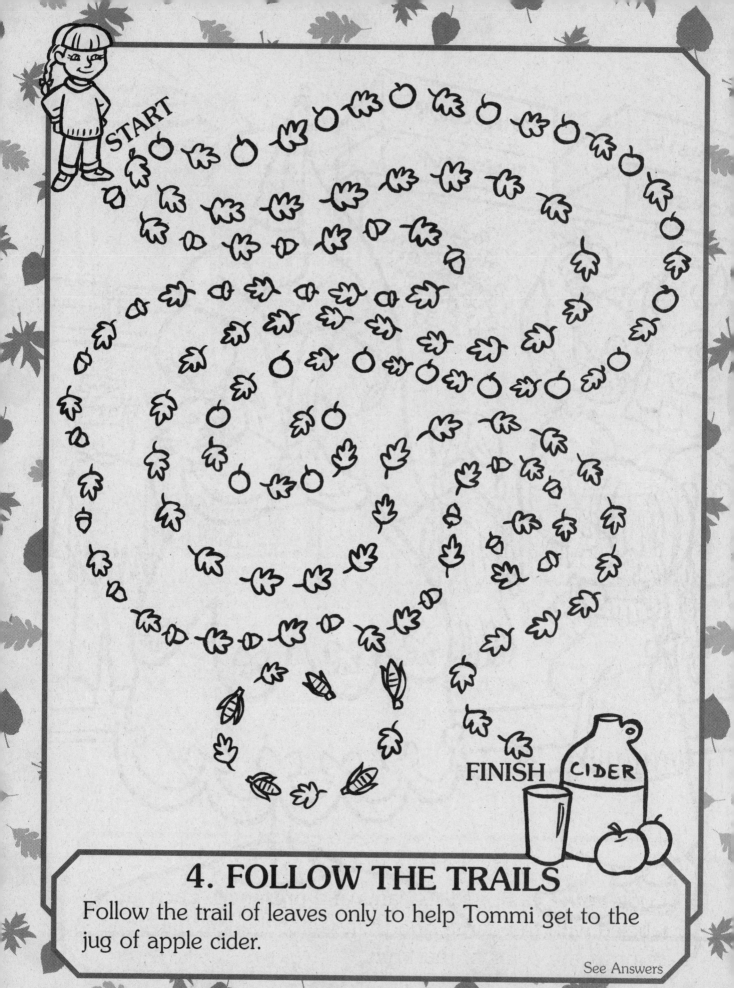

START

FINISH CIDER

4. FOLLOW THE TRAILS

Follow the trail of leaves only to help Tommi get to the jug of apple cider.

See Answers

3. FRUIT TREATS

Look at the jars of jellies, jams and preserves. Each jar is labeled with the name of a fruit. Color the jars the same color as the color of that fruit.

Looking for Halloween Costumes

Tommi names her pumpkin.

Reading Stories by the Fire

Unpacking the Cool Weather Clothes

SWEATERS

5. A FALL FAVORITE

Fill in every space that has a dot to see Tommi's favorite pajamas.

See Answers

A Pilgrim

Cooking the Thanksgiving Meal

A MEMORY GAME

Look at the picture. Then turn the page to play a
memory game.

Learning About the Pilgrims

1. There are three girls and one boy in the picture.

2. Tommi's sweater has a pumpkin on it.

3. Tommi's hair is braided.

4. Tommi's brother has a lollipop.

6. A MEMORY GAME

Think about the picture on the previous pages. Circle the sentences that are true.

See Answers

Fall Frolic

The Homecoming Parade

Flying South for the Winter

A Swirl of Leaves

A Decoration

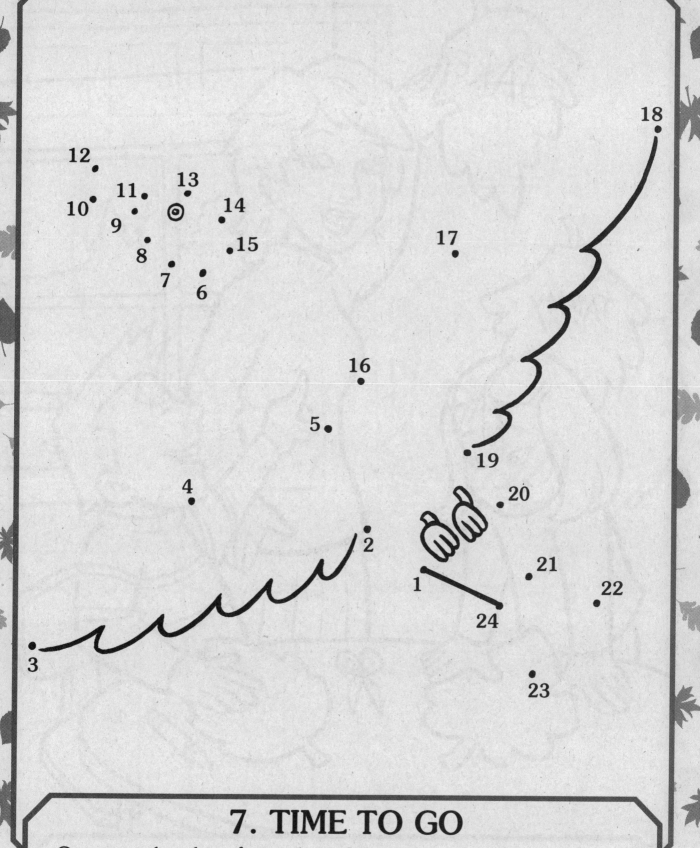

7. TIME TO GO

Connect the dots from 1 to 24 to see something that flies south for the winter.

See Answers

Making Thanksgiving Decorations

8. "J IS FOR..."

Tommi and her brother wear jackets early in the fall. Jacket begins with the letter J. Circle other things on this page that begin with the letter J.

See Answers

At the Farm

9. A THANKSGIVING FEAST

Look at the pictures of foods. Circle the ones that are commonly eaten on Thanksgiving.

See Answers

START

FINISH

10. TRICK-OR-TREATING

Tommi's brother wants to go trick-or-treating with his sister and her friends. Help him get to Tommi by finding a path through the maze.

See Answers

Making Candy Apples

A Pie Eating Contest

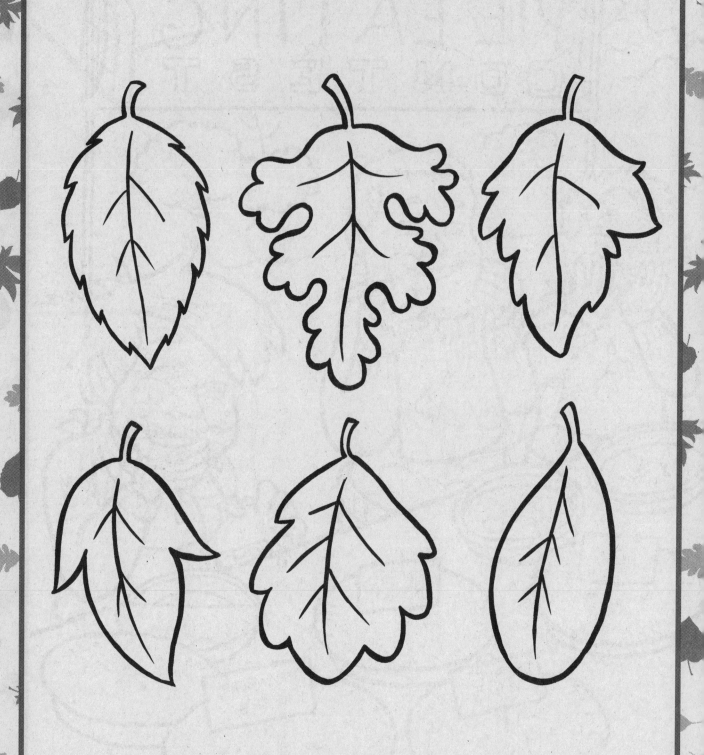

11. CHANGING COLORS

Leaves change colors in the fall. Look at the leaves.
Color them your favorite colors.

Tommi wishes on a star.

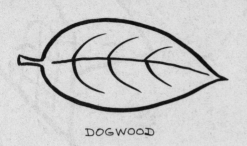

DOGWOOD

SASSAFRAS

SWEET GUM

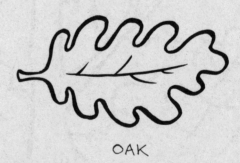

OAK

12. SHAPES

Leaves have different shapes. Look at the leaves, labeled with the type of tree each is from. Draw the leaves in the space next to each one.

13. WISHES CAN COME TRUE

Trace the star. Make a wish. Now draw what you wished for on the page.

Cuddly Bears

"Hoo, hoo, who will you be on Halloween?"

A Class Trip to the Pumpkin Patch

14. WHAT DOES NOT BELONG?

Circle the picture in each row that does not belong.

See Answers

Apple Butter from Farmer John's Orchard

Sharing a Nut

15. FIND THE HIDDEN ANIMALS

There are four creatures hidden in the pumpkin patch.
Find and circle them.

See Answers

A MEMORY GAME

Look at the pictures. Then turn the page to play a memory game.

16. A MEMORY GAME

Match each child with the activity they were doing in the picture on the previous pages.

See Answers

Creative Carving

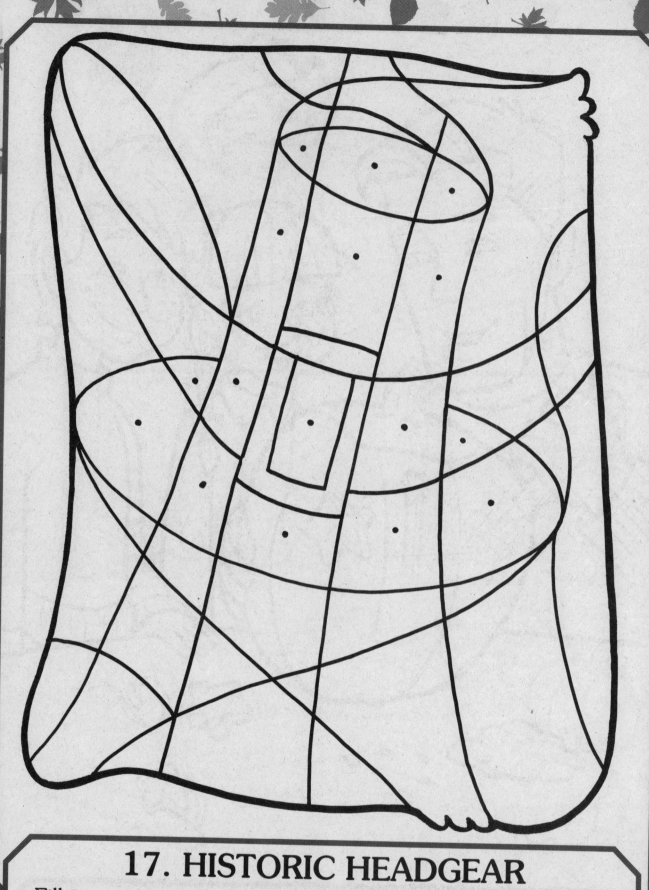

17. HISTORIC HEADGEAR

Fill in every space that has a dot to see what the pilgrim men wore on their heads.

See Answers

Farmer John's Garden

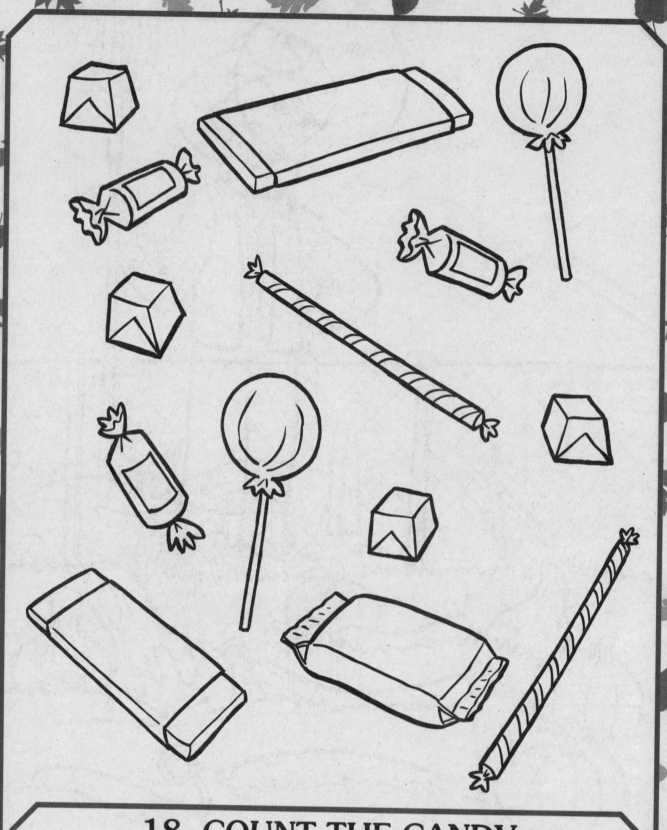

18. COUNT THE CANDY

Look at the Halloween candy. Circle three chewy candies.
Put an X over two candy bars. Draw a box around one
lollipop.

See Answers

September's full moon is known as the
Harvest Moon, or Corn Moon.

Visiting the Historic Village

19. COLOR-BY-NUMBER SCARECROW
Using the color code, color the scarecrow.

Color Code

1 = RED   2 = BLUE
3 = GREEN 4 = YELLOW
5 = ORANGE 6 = BLACK
7 = BROWN 8 = LT. BLUE

No two pumpkins are the same!

Hiding in the Leaves

20. WHERE DID THE BIRDS GO?

Farmer John's scarecrow scared off all of the birds. Find and circle five birds hidden in the picture.

See Answers

The Native Americans taught the pilgrims how to grow food in the new land.

Aunt Jane and Uncle Joe come for
Thanksgiving.

1

21. DRAW A TURKEY

Draw a turkey by tracing your hand. Place your thumb on the number 1 and spread your hand flat against the page. Trace the shape it makes. Color each finger like turkey feathers. The outline of your thumb is the turkey's head and neck. The palm is the body. Draw two legs to finish your turkey!

Snack Time

"Fall is our favorite season."

Answers

1.

ANSWERS
BUCKETS OF APPLES = 2
PIES = 3
WREATHS = 4

2.

4.

5.

Answers

6.

1. There are three girls and one boy in the picture.

2. Tommi's sweater has a pumpkin on it.

3. Tommi's hair is braided.

4. Tommi's brother has a lollipop.

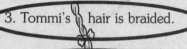

7.

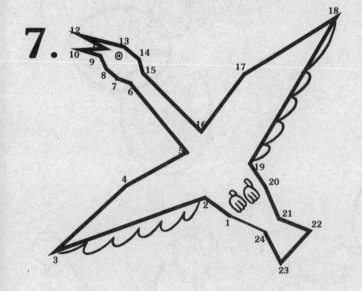

8.

9.

10.

Answers

14.

15.

16.

Answers

17. 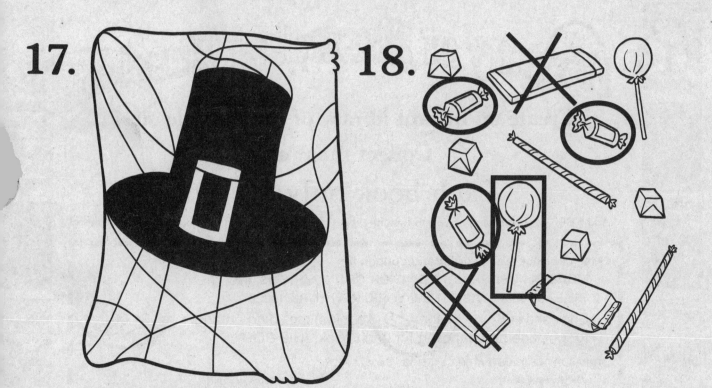 **18.**

20.

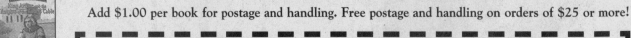

Treasury of Illustrated Classics™

Create an instant library of timeless classics!

Collect them all!

Each book only $2.99!

Add $1.00 per book for postage and handling. Free postage and handling on orders of $25 or more!

Mail check or money order and coupon to:

MODERN PUBLISHING, A DIVISION OF UNISYSTEMS, INC.

155 EAST 55th STREET, NEW YORK, NEW YORK 10022

Enclosed is $_____ for _____book(s) including an additional $1.00 for postage and handling for each book. (NO COD's)

TREASURY OF ILLUSTRATED CLASSICS - Series 1

Little Women (#39361)
Swiss Family Robinson (#39362)
20,000 Leagues Under the Sea (#39363)
The Legend of Sleepy Hollow & Rip Van Winkle (#39364)
Black Beauty (#39365)
Heidi (#39366)

The Secret Garden (#39367)
Anne of Green Gables (#39368)
Moby Dick (#39369)
Adventures of Huckleberry Finn (#39370)
Jane Eyre (#39371)
Treasure Island (#39372)

TREASURY OF ILLUSTRATED CLASSICS - Series 2

A Little Princess (#39341)
Rebecca of Sunnybrook Farm (#39342)
The Adventures of Tom Sawyer (#39343)
The Adventures of Robin Hood (#39344)
Peter Pan (#39345)
Robinson Crusoe (#39346)

The Adventures of Sherlock Holmes (#39347)
Gulliver's Travels (#39348)
The Call of the Wild (#39349)
Oliver Twist (#39350)
The Wizard of Oz (#39351)
Alice in Wonderland (#39352)

TREASURY OF ILLUSTRATED CLASSICS - Series 3

The Adventures of Pinocchio (#39306)
Beauty and the Beast (#39307)
The Time Machine (#39308)
Frankenstein (#39309)
Pygmalion (#39310)
The Wind in the Willows (#39311)

The Prince and the Pauper (#39312)
Journey to the Center of the Earth (#39313)
White Fang (#39314)
King Arthur and the Knights of the Round Table (#39315)
The Jungle Book (#39316)
Great Expectations (#39317)

NAME: _____

ADDRESS: _____

CITY: _____ STATE: _____ ZIP: _____

Please allow 4-6 weeks for delivery.
OFFER GOOD FOR UNITED STATES RESIDENTS ONLY.
™ Treasury of Illustrated Classics is a registered trademark of Modern Publishing, a division of Unisystems, Inc. All rights reserved.

6-05